# AMERICAN ELVES - THE YANKOOS

# THE YANKOOS

# AND

# THE OAK-HICKORY FOREST ECOLOGY

## BOOK FOUR

By Robert Frieders, Ph.D.

One of a Yankoo Series of Books

COVER:  Finian, the Yankoo naturalist, examines an old Hornets' nest that has fallen to the ground and broken open.

Yankoo Publishing Co.

# AMERICAN ELVES - THE YANKOOS

# THE YANKOOS

# AND

# THE OAK-HICKORY FOREST ECOLOGY

## BOOK FOUR

By Robert Frieders, Ph.D.

All photographs and line drawings by the author

Published by: The Yankoo Publishing Co.
10606 W. Cameo Drive
Sun City, AZ 85351-2708

Copyright 1996 by Robert Frieders

First Printing 1996

Printed in the United States of America

Library of Congress Catalog Card Number 93-61530

ISBN 0-9639284-3-0

## Acknowledgments

Dottie, our computer editor, and I wish to thank our friends who have helped make this book a reality.

**Our Consultant - Dr. Mamie Ross**
**Our Editor - Professor Marge Edwards**

We are all proud of this book on the plant and animal life of the Oak-Hickory Forest. It is our hope that each of you will consider yourself to be the "Friend" as you read this book. May the American Elves, the Yankoos, provide you with an interesting adventure as you learn about life in the forest..

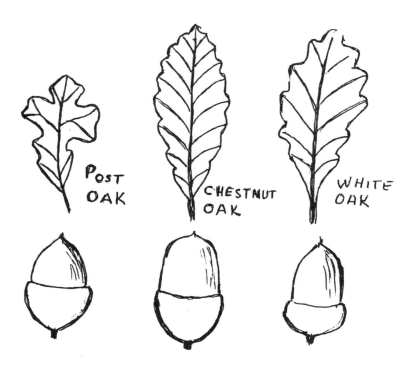

# Table of Contents

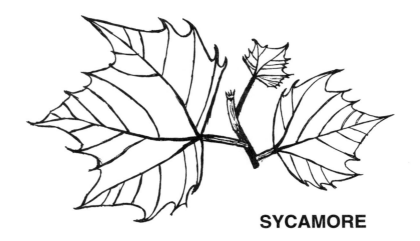

**SYCAMORE**

# CHAPTER ONE

## LESTER - ON HIS MAIL ROUTE

Lester admires an azalea that is blooming. It is an early flowering plant in our forest. The flower is a light pink color. This azalea sends up new plants from its roots. That is why we see so many clumps of this plant in our forest.

"HELLO, MY FRIEND!"

Come with me, my friend. We shall deliver the Yankoo mail together. Let me see whether I have a letter for Pierre.

I do indeed have a letter for him. His friend Angelo has written to him. Angelo lives in the Everglades. Angelo is also a chef. They say he prepares very tasty fish meals. Pierre told me that he had learned much from Angelo.

Let's go a little bit to the right, past that log. Wait a minute...I see something. Here, let me pick up this stick. Do you see where I am pointing?

See, it's a pile of leaves. The wind has pushed them up against those stones. Look carefully; there is a spider on those leaves.

I knew you would also spot that spider. It is hard to see. Its color blends in very well with the color of the leaves. The spider is lying in wait for an insect. An insect coming past would not see the spider until it was too late.

That spider would jump out and grab the insect - Gotcha!!  Spider food it would be.  That is a Wolf Spider.  It is one of the group of spiders called Hunting Spiders.  The Hunting Spiders live on the forest ground.  Not one of the Hunting Spiders spins a web.  Wolf spiders, like this one, lie in wait for an insect.  However, they can run fast and catch insects fleeing from them.

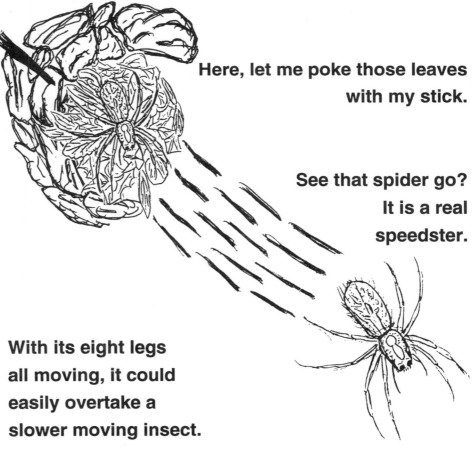

Here, let me poke those leaves with my stick.

See that spider go? It is a real speedster.

With its eight legs all moving, it could easily overtake a slower moving insect.

Here, let me sketch a spider head for you.

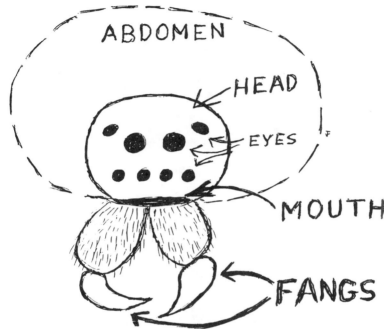

Imagine that you are looking head-on at a spider head. It would look like this. First, I make the spider's eyes. Spiders have many eyes. Most spiders have eight eyes; some have only six. Say, this spider has eight eyes. Then, the spider's mouth is next.

The mouth lies just below the head part with the eyes. Then come two hairy parts below the mouth. On the end of these parts are the fangs. All spiders have fangs. Most spiders also have poison glands. They inject poison into an animal through these fangs.

Here is a sketch I made of a spider that has caught a fly.

The spider catches the insect with its legs. Then, it pierces the insect's body with the sharp points of the fangs.

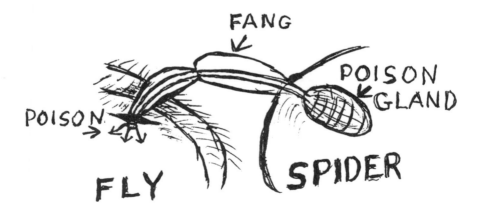

A fang is hollow. First, it pierces the insect's body. Then, it shoots poison through the fang into the insect. The poison passes through the opening at the sharp end of the fang.

The poison of many spiders can kill insects and even some small animals. Once the animal has been killed, the spider drinks the body fluids of the animal. Spiders do not eat solid food. They have no mouth parts like teeth to break up food. All spiders live on a liquid diet. They only eat liquids. The spider pushes its mouth against the animal. This forms, as it were, a "short straw". Then, it sucks out the liquids. After it has drained out all the liquids, the dry carcass is left as food for other forest animals.

Look over there, my friend. Do you see that spider? That is a female Wolf Spider. Notice the round egg sac. The spider has attached that round egg sac to its rear end. It will carry the sac there until the eggs hatch. The eggs will hatch into spiderlings, small spiders. The spiderlings make a hole in the egg sac wall and climb out.

I saw many spiderlings come out of an egg sac, one day.  So many were coming out that I thought to myself that we have a problem here.  Why does nature produce so many spiderlings for this area here?  Why is this happening?  This area does not have enough spider food to feed that many spiderlings.  The vast majority will surely starve to death.

As I watched, I made an interesting discovery.  After seeing what happened, I realized nature had solved this problem.  There will be no overpopulation of Wolf Spider spiderlings in this area.

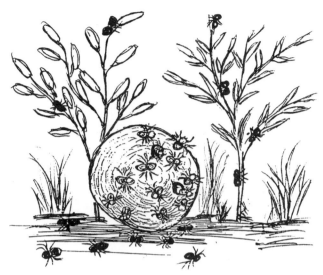

I watched the spiderlings come out of the holes in the egg sac. They crawled all over the area. Then, I saw the spiderlings climbing up the plants of the area. Some climbed to the very top of the plant. Others climbed out to the end of the long side branches. The spiderlings then shot out fine threads into the air from the spigots on their rear end.

ORIGINAL   BALLOONISTS
SPIDERLINGS

A gentle breeze in the area now took these spiderlings aloft.  You know, a small spider is very light.  The threads it made served as a balloon.  So, I watched as these spiderlings sailed out on their balloons.  Each will settle down in a new home in another part of the forest.  The overpopulation problem I worried about had been solved.  Nature had devised a unique transportation system for these spiderlings.  There were too many spiderlings in one spot.  So, nature had these spiderlings take to the air.  They are transported to areas where there are fewer Wolf Spiders.  The large population from the egg sac has been spread out in the forest.  Each new area will provide enough food for these spiderlings.  My friend, nature has solved what I thought would be a problem.  The solution shows a streak of genius.  Only nature could come up with such a solution.

There goes a Red Admiral butterfly. Notice how erratic its flight is. It looks like short jolts and jerks. That flight plan keeps it alive. Another animal would have a hard time catching it. It would never know which way the butterfly was going. Oh, look it has settled on that leaf. Notice how beautiful it is.

Notice the antennae of that butterfly. They come off the head. See how they are knobbed.

Those antennae pick up odors in the air.  Antennae pick up odors given off by the opposite sex.  It is quite possible the antennae also detect faint odors coming from food sources.

The Red Admiral and the Painted Lady butterflies are two common butterflies in our forest.  They can often be seen together in open sunlit areas.

Red Admiral eggs are laid on nettle plants.  A single egg is laid on a leaf.  After hatching, the caterpillar starts eating  nettle leaves.  It builds a place for itself to rest.  It bends over a leaf and ties the two bent sides together with silk strands.  Well, there it goes.  That flight pattern is really something.  This way, it goes; then, that way, it goes; and then, still a different way.  A predator has a problem trying to catch the Red Admiral!

Look over there, my friend. The forest Iris plants are blooming. Aren't they beautiful? Notice, they are receiving lots of sunlight.

The leaves of the trees have not developed, yet. They have not shaded that area at this time. As summer approaches, that area will be shaded. Very little, if any, sunlight will fall on it. The leaves above, on the trees, will take all the sunlight. So, the best time for that small Iris plant is now, springtime. It needs that sunlight to make food.

It grows above ground, using food stored in the rootstalk. Then, it makes food in that sunlight. Some food will make roots, leaves, flowers, and seeds. Other food will be stored in the rootstalk. Next year, that stored food will be used. It will be used to start the Iris on its life cycle. The small forest plants need sunlight to exist in our forest. In the springtime, the ground level areas receive sunlight. That is why one finds so many small plants in the springtime. Most small plants could not exist in the summer shade.

# CHAPTER TWO

## PIERRE - THE YANKOO CHEF

Look up ahead of us, my friend. That is Pierre's Yankoo Eatery. I see that Olaf, the Yankoo postmaster, and Joshua, the Yankoo doctor, are there. They come every day for a bowl of soup.

Hi, Pierre!  Hi, Olaf!  Hi, Joshua!

Hi, Lester!  Would you and your friend like a bowl of soup?  Olaf and Joshua say that it tastes good.  Yes indeed, my friend and I would enjoy a bowl of soup. I see it's gumbo vegetable soup.  It does taste good, Pierre.  You know, Pierre, my friend wondered what a Yankoo chef does all day.  Could you tell him what a chef's life is like?

Oh, I would be happy to do that, Lester.  My friend, the eatery opens early every morning.  It closes at sundown.  Hungry forest Yankoos drop by during the day for something to eat.  So, I always prepare a nice selection of items for them.  You know, a chef only prepares the food for the guests.  The forest Yankoos supply the food for the eatery.

Bruno, the baker, provides me with Yankoo loaves of bread and other pastries. See, there is the large loaf of Yankoo bread for today.

Icabod, the fisherman, supplies me with fresh fish.  See that catch of fish over there.  The middle fish is a Large Mouth Bass.  The top and bottom fishes are Small Mouth Bass.  They will make fine fillets for fish sandwiches.

Old Zeb supplies me with vegetables.  Old Zeb is the Yankoo gardener.  He grows many kinds of vegetables in an open spot in the forest.  He grows cabbages, carrots, onions, beans, potatoes, peas, and parsley.  Zephyr, the Yankoo deliveryman, brings all those items to the eatery as I need them.  You know, we Yankoos help one another.  So , you see, it is rather easy for a chef  with all the other Yankoos helping me.  Oh, I prepare some tasty dishes for forest Yankoos.  Hungry guests always enjoy a hearty meal.  Some prefer a fish sandwich special or a bowl of soup.  They come hungry.  When they leave my eatery, they are no longer hungry.

Often during the day, there are no Yankoo guests to feed.  Then, I observe my neighbors, a pair of chipmunks.  This is their area, too.  They scurry back and forth during the day.  If another chipmunk wanders in, it is driven away by this pair.  The nuts, seeds, berries, and other fruits here are theirs.  No chipmunk intruder is welcome.  These chipmunks have dug tunnels throughout this area.

See this opening here.  It goes straight down a few inches.  Then it connects with many underground tunnels.

There are many openings to these tunnels. They pop into one hole and come out a few seconds later from another hole in the ground. They have underground chambers coming off the tunnel network.

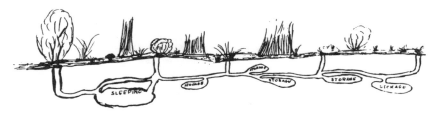

This sketch shows openings in the ground. Their tunnels and storage, I imagine, would look something like this.

You should see them when the acorns fall. They gather up the acorns. I have watched them many times. They pick up an acorn with their paws. Then, they bite off the sharp point on the acorn. The acorn is then put into a side cheek pouch.

A point on the acorn would cause injury to the cheek pouch. It must be bitten off. Then, into a cheek pouch on one side it goes. Then, another acorn is found. The point is bitten off. This one goes into the pouch

LINING OF MOUTH CAVITY

SKIN OF CHEEK

CHEEK POUCH

POUCH OPENING TO MOUTH CAVITY

on the other side. In short order, the two-side cheek pouches are full of acorns. It now has four acorns in each side pouch. One acorn is also held between its teeth. Down into the ground the chipmunk goes. It stores them in the food chamber. One might wonder why it needs these cheek pouches.

You know, collecting the winter nuts can be dangerous. The chipmunk can carry many acorns with the pouches. That means less dangerous collecting times. The hawks and fox have fewer times to catch the chipmunk.

Oh, Oh! Did you hear that whistle? There, it sounds again. That, my friend, is not a bird call. That is the chipmunk danger call. It stands upright on its hind legs and whistles. Then, it dives into the nearest hole in the ground. There it goes.

Sometimes, the danger is a Red Fox. If the fox is close, the chipmunk runs straight up the nearest tree trunk. Chipmunks have very pointed claws. They are very fast climbers. It would be safe from a Red Fox in a tree. The Red Fox, like other members of the dog family, cannot climb a tree. But it better not try escaping from a Gray Fox this way. Gray Foxes are also expert tree climbers. Above ground, a chipmunk must always be vigilant. Owls and hawks pose a danger from the air above. Red Fox, snakes, and weasels pose a danger on the ground. That is why the chipmunk has so many tunnels and so many entrances and exits from these tunnels.

Chipmunks store nuts, seeds, pine cones, and other dry foods underground.  These are their winter pantries.  Chipmunks eat many things.  I have observed them eating berries and fruits. They will

nibble on the forest mushrooms. They also catch and eat snails, mice, young birds, and small snakes.  On cold and rainy days, chipmunks stay underground. It is in the fall when they are very active. Storing acorns underground for winter food comes first. Then, the chipmunk stores nuts all over the territory. Here, some are stored under a pile of leaves.  In another area, acorns are pushed under a clump of grass plants.  Next year, the chipmunk will not remember many of these storage places.  Many nuts will start growing in those places. So, the chipmunk is really a forester. It plants trees - nut trees - its favorite kind of tree. Underground, the chipmunks have an enlarged den area. They sleep there at night.

On rainy, cold, and very hot days, the chipmunks stay underground for the most part. The pair by the eatery raised six young last year. The young come above ground when they are still rather small. It doesn't take long, and they are full grown. When full grown, they leave this area. They must settle down in another forest area. As the winter approaches, chipmunks eat more food. They become quite fat. When winter is here, they stay underground.

They curl up in a deep sleep. They awaken every so often to eat some food. Then, back to sleep they go. Come a warm day in spring, out they come! They are rather slim and have a trim shape. There will be lots of activity now after that long winter sleep.

So that, my friend, is what this Yankoo chef does during a day. My first concern is always to feed my fellow Yankoos. They come into the eatery hungry. They no longer leave hungry. Sometimes, it is a tasty fish sandwich or a bowl of gumbo vegetable soup. Or, if the Yankoo is really hungry, I have a full-course meal for my guest. Then, at  slack eatery times, I enjoy observing and learning more about that pair of chipmunks.

Thank you, Pierre. My friend and I have enjoyed the tasty soup. We also have learned much about those chipmunks. Pierre, Bruno has given me a birthday cake. Could you take the cake? Give a piece to each Yankoo guest. Lester, every Yankoo dropping in today at the eatery shall have a piece. Oh, yes, Pierre, here is your letter. Thanks, Lester. Goodbye, Olaf. Goodbye, Joshua. We must be off on our mail route. Thanks for the soup, Pierre.

Look over there at that toad, my friend.  That toad must be hungry.

You know, toads belong to the forest night crew. They come out at night to find food.  Here it is daytime.  That toad is still hunting for food.  It must be very hungry.  At this time of day,  it is normally asleep.  Look at that toad.  It sits there without moving.  But just  let an insect come near.  Gotcha!! Toad food that insect would be.

You know, it does not have to run to catch food.
No.  The toad does it the easy way.  Let the food
come to you.  However, if no food comes, it must
move.  It moves to another area.  It moves to an area
where there are insects.  The toad will then sit there
motionless.  Insects move here and there on the
forest floor.  The toad blends in with the litter.

Insects come closer and closer.  When within range,
out goes the toad's tongue.  That toad's tongue can
flip out a distance in front of that toad.  It is not
attached back in the throat like most animals'
tongues.  No, it is attached just inside the very front
of the lower jaw.

That long sticky tongue flips out.  The end wraps around the insect.  Back into the mouth, it goes.

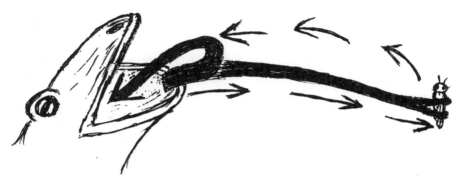

All this happens very fast.  Now, you see that insect; now, you don't.  The tongue places the insect in the back of the mouth cavity.  It will shortly be in the toad's stomach.

Toads, you know, do not have teeth.  They do not chew food.  They eat all their food whole.  The toad has short  legs.  The toad's body is rather chunky.

TOADS HOP

Toads move by hopping. Their hind legs propel them forward a short distance.

FROGS LEAP

The frogs differ from toads in this aspect. Frogs have very long legs. Those legs propel the frog in a very long leap. To cover the same distance, a toad would have to hop a lot. You know, we Yankoos have short legs. We are like the toads. If we wish, we can hop. However, we can also walk. But we Yankoos would never be great jumpers.

GLAND

Many animals leave the toad alone. Notice that large gland on the toad. That gland secretes a poison. If a predator contacted that poison once, it would never bother a toad again.

Toads, like frogs, produce mating sounds. Notice the large ear membrane by the eye. This picks up sound waves.

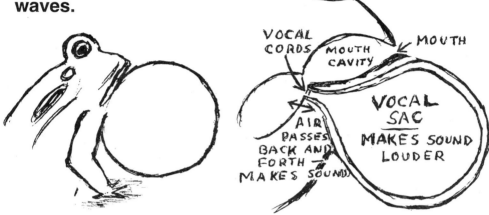

Toads have a vocal sac just inside their throat area. Air is put into the vocal sac swelling it. Then, air moves over the vocal cords producing the sound. The male-mating sound attracts the female. They mate. The female lays strings of gelatinous-covered eggs in the water. The eggs hatch into small tadpoles. The tadpoles eat plants and grow in size. They eventually lose the tail. Legs grow on the tadpoles. When mature, they spend more time on land. Toads eat insects. Our toads stay under the forest litter on hot days. Often, they rest under moist litter leaves. Sometimes, I have seen them in a hole in the ground. They dig the hole and have dirt covering them. It's much cooler there on a hot day.

Oh, look at those small flowering plants, my friend. That plant is called Pipsissewa.

Notice, the leaves are dark green. There is a white stripe in the middle of the leaf. Many plants make up that clump. Most of the plants are flowering. Each plant usually has two flowers. The forest insects pollinate these flowers. Once pollinated, the plants produce seeds. There are many of these plants in our forest.

# CHAPTER THREE


# LESTER MEETS METHUSELAH

Oh, look at that large turkey, my friend. That is a large hen turkey. See how it blends in with the forest vegetation.

Look at what we have up ahead, my friend. There is a group of turkeys. These turkeys roam through our forest all year. Notice how large those birds are. They have a wingspread of some four or five feet. Usually, these groups have one male turkey along with a number of hens. By day, they spend their time on the ground. At night, they roost sitting on a branch in a tree.

In the spring, the male attracts the hens by gobbling. This gobbling sound can be heard for quite a distance. Soon, a number of hens have been drawn to the spot. Then, the male displays its tail feathers. Here is a drawing

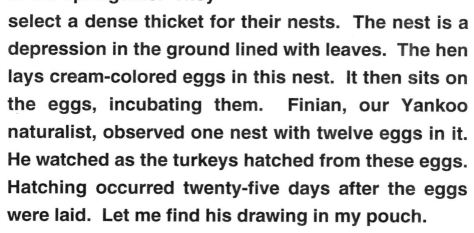

of male tail feathers being displayed. With tail feathers displayed, the male struts back and forth in front of the hens. The male is out to impress the hens. Normally, the male tail feathers look like this.

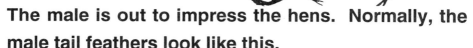

Turkeys nest in our forest in the springtime. They select a dense thicket for their nests. The nest is a depression in the ground lined with leaves. The hen lays cream-colored eggs in this nest. It then sits on the eggs, incubating them. Finian, our Yankoo naturalist, observed one nest with twelve eggs in it. He watched as the turkeys hatched from these eggs. Hatching occurred twenty-five days after the eggs were laid. Let me find his drawing in my pouch.

Here it is.  The chick inside
the egg has an egg
tooth.  Notice that
sharp pointed
structure. It's
located on the tip of
the upper beak.  That is the egg tooth.  The chick uses
that tooth to get out of its shell.  Here is how it
hatches from the egg.  The chick makes a hole in the
shell with that sharp point.

SHELL

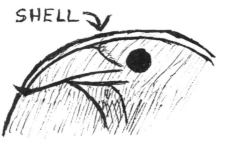

Then, it starts cutting the
egg shell in a circular
fashion.  Here is a drawing
Finian made of the hatching
process.  When the circle
has been completed, out
comes the chick.  As you see,
a young turkey works hard getting out of its shell.

At first, the young turkeys nest at night under the wings and tail feathers of the hen.  After several weeks, they begin roosting in trees at night.  Turkeys have two feeding periods each day.  Early in the morning, they leave their roost and begin feeding. Here is a picture of the young birds following the hen on their feeding trip.

Turkeys have strong toes.  They are ideal for scratching.  They kick the leaf litter on the ground backward.  These scratching marks are wider at the back than in the front.  Here is a drawing Finian made of a turkey scratching mark.
The forest litter is kicked backward.  That uncovers the plant and animal food under the leaves.

Their scratchings uncover other kinds of food. They uncover beetles, centipedes, millipedes, snails, and other insects.

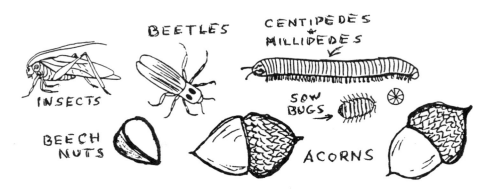

The main food of our turkeys is the forest acorns. They eat acorns all year except in the summer. Come summer, the acorns produced the year before cannot be eaten. Some of those acorns have rotted. Others have sprouted into oak seedlings. So, in the summertime, turkeys eat other food. They feast on strawberries, blackberries, and huckleberries. In the summer, the days are long. The turkeys rest a lot around mid-day. They will feed again before they go to roost. Before or just after sundown, they fly into a tree. They will roost there through the night. Turkeys roost squatting on a branch. They sleep with their breasts against a branch.

There go our turkeys, my friend.  See how they are traveling.  They almost proceed in a single file.  Well, they will be resting soon.  It is about noon.

Well, let's be on our way to deliver mail to Gramps.

Look, my friend, there is Methuselah.  He is in that patch of May Apples.  He sees us.

Hi, Methuselah!  Hi, Lester!  I see you have a friend with you today.  Yes, my friend and I are delivering the Yankoo mail together.  We have seen many wonders of our forest on the way.

What are you doing, Methuselah?  Oh, I am studyiny these May Apples.  They are very interesting plants. Here is a picture of several coming through the leaves of the forest.

The plant's leaves are like an umbrella.  They look like a closed umbrella.  After the plant comes through the forest leaves, the umbrella opens up.  The mature plant has two leaves branching off a plant stock.

See how the open leaves make the plant look like an umbrella.

Where the two leaves branch off, a flower will form. The flower is waxy white. It has six or nine petals. The flowers are pollinated especially by the bumblebees. The flower forms the fruit and seeds. The seeds develop inside an apple-like fruit. The root, stem, and leaves of this plant are all poisonous. When ripe, the fruit is eaten by forest animals.

See all these plants here. They did not grow from seeds. No, they all probably grew from the underground roots of other May Apple plants. Underground their roots are interconnected.

As new roots are made by a plant, additional new plants grow up from them. So, this large patch is always growing. Very few new plants grow from May Apple seeds. Most of the new plants grow from the roots of other plants. Many woodland flowers form large forest clumps in this way.

Well, Lester, I must continue my study. I am making a record of plants right here today. Next year, I will come back. I will then record how many new plants are here. They will develop from these interconnecting roots. Glad to have met you, my friend. Goodbye, Lester! Goodbye, Methuselah!

You know, my friend, Methuselah is a "stickler" for details. That is the only way to do it. He says this is the way it is. Well, you can be sure he is right. He thinks things through very carefully. Well, let's be off on our mail route.

# CHAPTER FOUR

## GRAMPS - THE YANKOO ELDER

Late in the afternoon, the raccoons become active. Here are several at the forest's edge. That black area by their eyes looks like a face mask. Both raccoons are surveying the scene.

**My friend, look what we have ahead of us.  That is a young raccoon.**

**Here, we will go around it.  Good, it is going the other way.  That is a very young raccoon.**

There, up ahead, is Gramp's hut. He has seen us. He is coming to greet us.

Hi, Lester. I see you have a friend with you.
Hi, Gramps. Yes, indeed, I do have a friend. He is learning about the forest and the Yankoos. Gramps, we saw a very young raccoon on our path. Oh, that is a friend of mine, Lester.
I saw it by a tree one morning. It looked like it was lost. I gave it some fruit.

It also ate some acorns. It has been around here for about five days. I have been watching a female raccoon with four young ones. They have a nest in a hollow tree nearby. Every day, the female takes the young on short trips. Then, I noticed the trips lasted a little longer. One day, I was down by our nearby stream. There were those raccoons. I saw the mother catch a crayfish. Soon, those young were catching crayfish. I have also seen them catch and eat frogs by the stream. The raccoons are very active at night. One day, I heard a bird calling out in distress. I wandered over to the area. The young raccoon was eating the bird's eggs.

You know, that young raccoon could be one of those I have been watching. Let's go back to my hut, Lester. Just look! There is that raccoon up against my hut.

There it goes.  It will wander away.  Here, let me show you its picture.  I took this the day I first saw it.

It looks a little lost, doesn't it?  Here is your letter, Gramps.  Oh, thank you, Lester.  It is from Ebenezer. Ebenezer, my friend, lives out in Desert Land.  He is a prospector.  It will be good to find out what Ebenezer has been doing out there.

Well, we must be off, Gramps.  Goodbye.

Goodbye, Lester.  Goodbye to your friend, too.  Come by again sometime.

My friend, look at that hornets' nest. See it up there in that tree. That is a rather large nest. Last year, a colony of hornets lived in that nest. Last fall, the new queens left that nest. After mating with these queens the males died.

Then, cold weather killed all the female workers in the nest. So now, the nest is empty. It will not be used this year. The hornets will make new nests for this year.

The only hornets alive in our forest this spring are the fertilized queens.  They were produced last fall.  They mated with the males then.  Each queen selected some protected spot to spend the winter.

Here, let me get out my drawing pad.  I will draw some pictures for you of the hornet and its nest. Those hornets have an interesting life cycle. Here is a picture of a hornet.  It is an insect.  It has two pairs of wings.  I stay away from these hornets.  They sting and it hurts.  Then that area swells up.  Joshua, our Yankoo doctor, says, "Stay away from those hornets. If you don't you'll be sorry."  So, I keep my distance.

This spring, those queens are already busy.  First, the queen selected a spot for the nest.  Then, it set about securing material to make the nest.  It probably went to a rotted  trunk like this one.

There, the queen bit off some wood. It chewed this wood.  Along with the hornet's saliva, it became a pulp. That pulp becomes nest material.  The queen  then fashioned this pulp into nest parts.

First, the pulp was glued to the branch. Then, it was extended down. At the wider end, cells were made. Into each cell, the queen laid an egg. It made a gray paper-like covering over the nest.

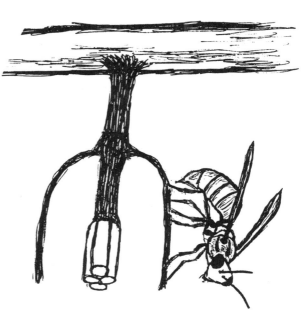

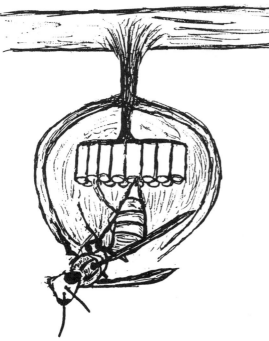

Then, it constructed more cells. It enlarged the nest. Into each cell, the queen laid an egg. Then, it fashioned a thicker, gray, paper-like covering over the nest.

This is about what the queen has done so far this spring. About now, the eggs are hatching. A worm-like larva is hatching in each cell. The queen now must secure food for these larvae. The queen captures insects. It chews up the insects. This material is fed to the larvae. The larvae grow to mature size. Then, they change into hornets. The hornets produced are all females. These will be the workers in the nest. These female workers do not lay eggs. They are all sterile. Only the queen produces eggs. The new female workers now take over nest construction.

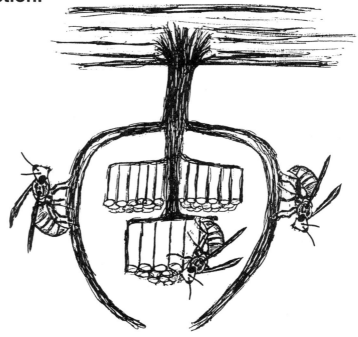

They tear down old portions.  They enlarge and make new cell areas.  They construct new pillars, new hexagonal combs.  They eat the old outer covering. They make a new larger covering.  The female workers also hunt for food for the larvae.  They capture flies, bees, insect larvae, moths, and butterflies.  All are chewed into smaller bits.  Then, this is fed to the larvae.  In the meantime, the queen is busy laying an egg in each cell. The hornets' nest becomes larger and wider.  The nest hangs down from the branch. The opening to the nest is at the bottom.

In late summer, the workers make large cells. The queen will lay a fertilized egg in each cell. These will now develop into new queens. Into other large cells, the queen lays unfertilized eggs. These will develop into males. These eggs now develop into larvae. They are fed and become mature. The cell is sealed off for each mature larva. Inside, each changes into a  hornet. When they emerge, the new queens leave the nest. The males follow. They will mate with these queens. The males will die in a short time. The fertilized new queens seek a protected spot. They will spend the winter there. As cold weather sets in, the female workers in the hive all die. The nest is now empty. When spring comes, a new nest will be made, just like we showed you.

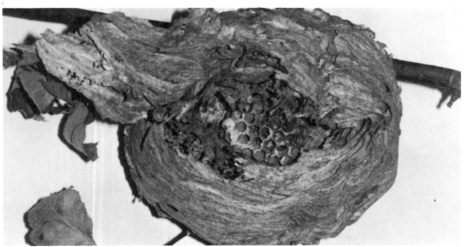

Here are some pictures of a hornets' nest. Finian took these pictures. He has studied these insects. Finian told me all about their life cycle.

Here is a picture of a hornets' nest. It is somewhat oval shaped. Part of the gray paper-like covering has been removed. This covering sheds the water when it rains. There are several layers of this material making the covering. This would provide for some air space between the layers. Such a setup should make a nest warmer inside on cold nights. It also should make a nest cooler on very hot days. Layers of air are good insulators.

Here is an excellent picture showing parts of two combs of cells.  A smaller comb is on the bottom of the wider comb.  Notice, not all the cells have been constructed.

Look at  those cell openings. They have six sides.  A six-sided structure is called a hexagon.  So, the hornet cells are hexagon in shape.  Notice how all of them are exactly the same size.  It is amazing how that hornet can make each and every one exactly the same shape.

Here is another picture. It shows a number of combs in the nest. There is a space between the combs. That space is needed. The queen has to lay eggs in each cell. Then, the workers daily have to feed the developing larvae. Finally, the new hornets have to come out. So, space is needed between the combs.

This last picture shows a smaller nest of these hornets. Many of these cells have been capped. The larvae inside are changing into hornets. Other cells are empty. The hornets have already emerged from those cells. One hornet head can be seen coming out of a cell.

Well, my friend, you now know about the hornets. Let's be off on our mail route.

# CHAPTER FIVE

## LESTER - ON HIS MAIL ROUTE

Look up ahead, my friend. There is the Acorn Weather Station. Rufus keeps the Yankoos informed. He has a number of weather stations in the forest. Today is warm and breezy. Zephyr, the Yankoo deliveryman, helps post the weather on these signs. Rufus decides what the weather will be. Zephyr posts what Rufus has predicted the weather will be.

Look up ahead, my friend. There is Finian. You have met Finian before. He is our Yankoo naturalist. He studies plants and animals of our forest. We, Yankoos, learn much from his observations. He is studying a Tent Caterpillar web.

Hi, Finian. Hi, Lester. Greetings to your friend, too. I am busy studying these Tent Caterpillars. During the winter months, I saw the egg mass here. The eggs were covered by a brown layer of foam material. The eggs are always laid in a crotch of branches. As leaves appear on this tree, the small caterpillars emerge from the eggs.

They begin to construct a small tent using the crotch branches. The tent has several layers of silk material. There are two openings to the tent.

Early in the morning, the caterpillars head out for food.

As they go, they leave a silk trail on the branch. As they move from one eaten leaf to another leaf, they leave the trail of silk.

After an hour or so, they follow the silk trail back to the tent. I have observed that they feed about noontime. When they return, they work on the tent. Later in the afternoon, they head out to feed again. They stay longer in the afternoon. This is usually the longest feeding period in a day.

When they return, they set about working on the tent.

The tent floor accumulates a lot of droppings. It also accumulates the skins the caterpillars have shed. As the caterpillars grow to a mature size,they shed their skin five times. When they shed their tight skin, we say they moult. The skin splits near the head. It is then worked backwards off the animals. The new skin they make is much larger. The caterpillars will now grow into larger size skins.

So, the droppings and shed skins litter the tent floor. As this occurs, a new floor is made over the old floor. The tent is made larger to house the bigger caterpillars.

During the season, the tent grows larger and larger.

TENT CATERPILLAR MOTH

When the caterpillars are mature, they drop to the ground. They seek a place on the ground to change into a pupal stage. I have found them on the bark of a tree, on fallen logs, and among the forest litter on the ground. The adult moths emerge in the middle of the summer. They mate. Then, the females lay the eggs on the trees. I have noticed they prefer the Wild Cherry trees in this area. This year, we have a great abundance of Tent Caterpillars. They have practically eaten all the leaves on some trees.

The Tent caterpillars are protected when they are in the silken tent. However, when they are out feeding, they are vulnerable. Some beetles and wasps feed on these caterpillars. Some years, we have many Tent Caterpillars. In other years, there are only a few here and there. The winter weather conditions could be involved. Finian, we must be going now. Goodbye. Goodbye, Lester. You and your friend have a nice day.

There are some beautiful forest flowers. They are pink in color. They are called Bouncing Bet. One finds them alongside our forest.

Look over here, my friend.  Do you see that clump of white plants?  Notice, the plants are growing through the leaves there.  Those are Indian Pipe plants.

That white larger part is the flower.  The whole plant looks like a pipe, doesn't it?

Once that flower is pollinated, the whole plant turns black.  That wide, white stem becomes thinner.  It shrivels.  It now looks like a thin black twig.  The flower parts now drop off the plant.  That curved flower-end of the plant now straightens up.  The flower enlarges into a capsule.  Inside this capsule, many very small seeds are formed.  When the seeds mature, the capsule opens.  Those small seeds now lie exposed to the wind.  The wind will pick up those seeds.  It will carry the seeds to new areas of the forest.  Those seeds, given moisture, will germinate.  They will produce an Indian Pipe plant.  But to do this, the plant must recycle.

Let me explain it to you this way, my friend. All plants and animals are made up of building blocks. These building blocks are called organic units. Plants that are green make these building blocks - these organic units. They make them "from scratch". They use water, carbon dioxide, and minerals. Green plants, growing in sunlight, use these materials and make them into building blocks.

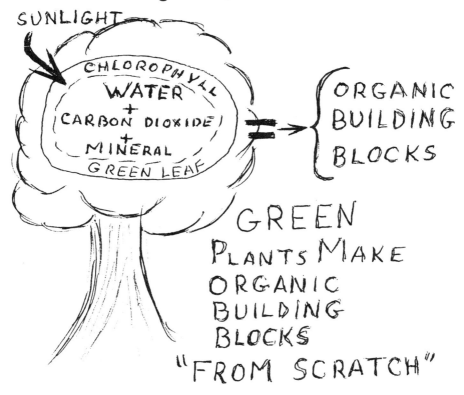

Only green plants make these building blocks "from scratch".

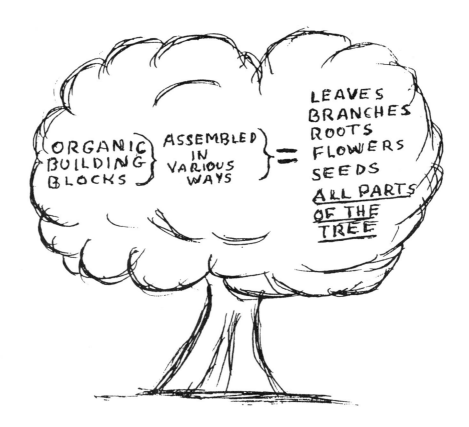

The plant assembles these building blocks into plant parts. Put together this way, the plant makes leaves. Put together another way, the plant makes flowers. Roots, stems, branches, and winter buds are all made from these building blocks. So, plants first make organic building blocks "from scratch". Then, they assemble these blocks in various patterns making all the plant structures.

Animals and non-green plants cannot make organic building blocks "from scratch". However, non-green plants and animals are built from these blocks. They must secure these blocks to grow and live. Since they cannot make them "from scratch", they must recycle. They must get some that are already made. Let's explain it with this caterpillar.

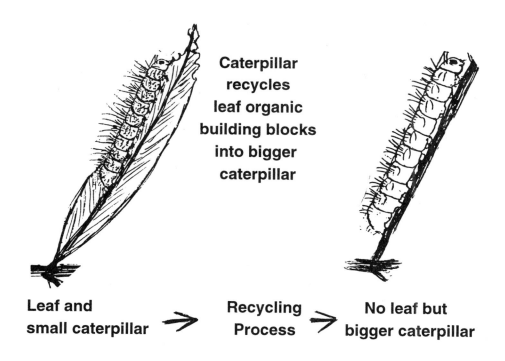

Caterpillar recycles leaf organic building blocks into bigger caterpillar

Leaf and small caterpillar → Recycling Process ⟩ No leaf but bigger caterpillar

So animals recycle. They digest plant food. They recycle the building blocks from plant to animal structures.

The Indian Pipe plant is not a green plant. So, the Indian Pipe plant cannot make organic units "from scratch". So, it must recycle. It must obtain building blocks. Then, it must assemble these blocks into Indian Pipe. It obtains the building blocks it needs from the forest litter.

You know that in a forest many things fall to the ground every day. There are dead leaves, flowers, seeds, twigs, and branches, just to mention a few things. All these materials are broken down continually into organic building blocks. They are broken down by fungi. These fungi plants are not green. They cannot make organic building blocks "from scratch". They break down the forest litter into these organic building blocks. Then, they use these building blocks.

These fungi use building blocks to make more fungi. They recycle. The fungi plants make recycling of the litter possible. Fungi break down the forest litter. They reduce the litter to organic building blocks. Now, these building blocks are present in the soil litter. They become available to other plants and animals. Many plants and animals can use these. They recycle.

The Indian Pipe benefits. It is not green in color. It cannot make organic building blocks "from scratch". It will use the building blocks made available by the fungi. They are there in the soil. All that is needed is to take them into the Indian Pipe plant.

Given moisture, the Indian Pipe seed will germinate. It grows into a tiny thread-like structure. It takes in organic building blocks from the soil. It makes more underground Indian Pipe. The plant takes in more and more building blocks. The plant begins to grow up through the forest litter. It continues growth until it is mature. The whole plant was made up of recycled building blocks. The fungi had broken down the soil debris into these building blocks. These organic building blocks were available in the soil. The Indian Pipe plant used these building blocks. A mature plant was made from them.

# CHAPTER SIX

## RUFUS - THE YANKOO WEATHERMAN

Look up ahead, my friend. We are coming to Rufus, the Yankoo weatherman. There he is. He is looking through his telescope. He is studying the cloud formation there in the sky. Hi, Rufus! Hi, Lester! Glad to see you and your friend. I was just studying those clouds. I believe we will have rain tomorrow. Sounds good, Rufus! The forest needs some rain. Rufus, I see the Crested Flycatcher perched there on your roof. Yes, Lester, it is always nearby. Every year it nests in a nearby tree. It uses an old woodpecker hole. It catches many insects here.

Lester, today I saw our Monarch butterflies again. You know, they all left us last fall. Well, today I saw a pair of Monarchs. Rufus, tell my friend about this butterfly. Oh, I will, Lester.

My friend, these Monarch butterflies are travelers. In late summer and fall, our Monarch butterflies leave us. They travel singly in a  southwesterly direction. They fly at ground level most of the time. In one day, a butterfly can cover some 20 to 25 miles. As they go, they feed on the nectar of fall flowers. Late in the afternoon, a migrant will stop at a tree. It will stay there for the night.

Other migrants, coming along, will also stop for the night. Next day, the early sun warms their bodies. Then, one by one, the migrants continue on their long journey. In early November, they arrive at their destination.

They will spend the winter there in the mountain area of Mexico. In January and February they move down to the valleys. Monarch butterflies in Canada and the United States, east of the Rocky Mountains, migrate to this spot. The Monarch butterflies, west of the Rocky Mountains, head down the western coast. They spend the winter in the Monterey penisula of California.

You know, those butterflies have covered a lot of territory. Some from Canada have traveled 2,000 miles. The butterflies spend the winter there. They cluster in trees near the top of the mountains. In mid February, the Monarch butterflies start their spring migration. Those in Mexico head out in a northeastern direction. The California migrants head north up the coastal area. All the migrants will be gone by middle or late March.

Many fly high and fast. Some continue flying day and night. They fly almost all the time. The females have mated with males at the winter site or along the way.

The Milkweed plants can be found almost everywhere along their routes. Some females stop along the way to lay eggs on the plants. In March and early April, Monarch larvae are already eating Milkweed leaves in southern areas. There may even be some new adult butterflies. It is early April here. The butterflies have already arrived. By May and June, they will be in northeastern United States and Canada.

That Milkweed plant is poisonous to most animals. The larvae eat these toxic leaves. Now, this poisonous material is in their bodies. The toxic material becomes part of the caterpillar.

Most predators will not try to eat Monarch caterpillars. Even adult butterflies have toxic materials in their bodies. Predators that try eating a Monarch once will never try again. So, the Monarch butterfly and larvae benefit greatly. Being poisonous to predators saves many a Monarch's life.

Look over here, Lester.  Here are two Monarch butterflies. The lighter-colored one is the female.  The brightly-colored one is the male.

Look at the hind wings of that male.  Do you see the enlarged black spot on the vein?  That is the alar gland.  It is a patch of scent scales. The male gives off an odor from this spot.  The odor is attractive to the females.  All wings of butterflies are made up of two membranes.  In between the membranes are the veins. See the veins on those Monarch butterflies.

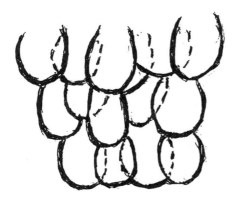

**Scales on the wing**

The wings and body are covered with very small scales. These scales have a projection that fits into a socket in the wing. The scales overlap one another on the wings. The scales look like colored spots.

**Scale with projection**

Leaf

**Egg on underside of leaf**

Inside a fertilized egg, materials are rearranged into a very small caterpillar. It will now break out of the egg. Many caterpillars eat the egg covering. Then, they start eating leaves. Female butterflies select favorite food plants. Eggs are deposited on these plants. Caterpillars have different preferences regarding leaves. Most caterpillars will not eat just any leaf. The Monarch caterpillar eats only Milkweed leaves.

As they eat the leaves, the caterpillars grow in size. They moult a number of times. In moulting, the caterpillar shakes off the old, tight skin covering. Now, it grows into a much larger skin.

The old skin splits behind the head. It is forced backwards to the rear of the caterpillar. Then, it is dropped off. Many caterpillars eat the old skin. Now, the caterpillar has a larger skin. The larger skin is folded to allow for expansion.

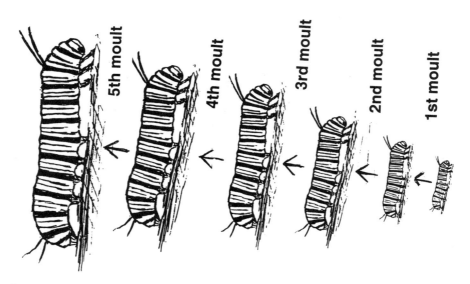

So, caterpillars moult. The Monarch moults five times.

When mature, the caterpillar attaches its rear end to a twig. Then, it changes its shape.

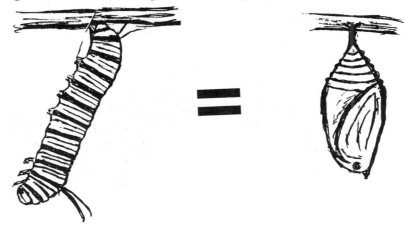

It  now is called a chrysalis.  Inside,caterpillar parts are broken down.  The units are now made into a butterfly.Then, out comes the adult butterfly.  All butterflies go through this life cycle.   Once the butterfly emerges, the wings become extended.  They become dry and firm.  Then, the butterfly flies!

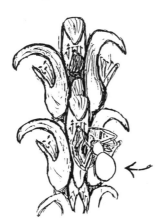

The butterfly now finds flowers. It will live on the flower's nectar.  Notice the crab spider on the flower. It lies in wait for bees and, also, butterflies.

Here is a picture of our forest Tiger Swallowtails. The two top pictures are of male butterflies. Males are always yellow in color. The bottom two butterflies are female butterflies. The color of a female Tiger Butterfly can vary. In the east and south, some are yellow colored females. Others are black colored females. Out west though, the female Tiger Swallowtail is always yellow. Oh, we have many beautiful butterflies in our forest. Well, I must get busy figuring out my weather report. Thank you Rufus. We always learn a lot from you. We must be on our mail route. Goodbye, Rufus. Goodbye, Lester.

Look at this picture of a Milkweed seed pod, my friend.

The pod has matured. It has split open. The seeds are being pulled out by the wind. Each seed has a silken parachute. The wind will carry these seeds to many areas. Many Milkweed plants will be produced. Monarch caterpillars will have abundant food.

Look at that rotting tree trunk, my friend.  Notice, something has been tearing it up.  It was probably our Pileated Woodpeckers.  Let's look for the Bess or Peg Beetle in that material.  They have galleries running through the rotted wood.  Look over here.  I have found some.

See, there are two larvae of the Peg Beetle.  These larvae eat the rotting wood.  They make many tunnels.  Sometimes, one finds colonies of adults and larvae in a log.  The larvae and adult beetles make a sound.

The adult beetles rub the roughened areas of the hind wings against the abdomen. This produces the sound. One can hear the sound. Here, I'll knock against the log - hear that sound! It is a faint but rather shrill sound. It could be that the Pileated Woodpecker hears those beetles. Oh, look here. There is an adult Peg or Bess Beetle.

Our Pileated Woodpecker will find this rotten log again. There is much woodpecker food still there.

Do you hear that bird call, my friend?  There it goes again - TWEE-TWEE.  That is the song of the Towhee. I often hear and see Towhees when I deliver the mail. Here comes the bird.  See, it has settled on those leaves.

That is a male Towhee.  It has a black-colored back. The back of the female Towhee is brown.  That bird will scatter those leaves with its feet.  This uncovers the animals living beneath the leaf litter.  Oh, many animals live there.

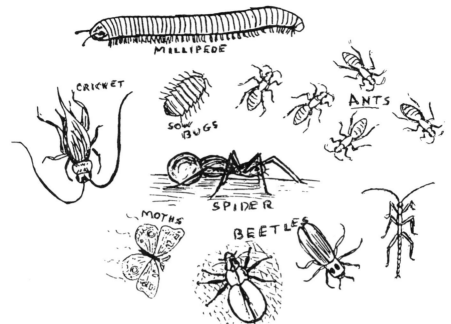

The Towhee finds beetles, ants, spiders, daddy long-legs, moths, sowbugs, millipedes and snails. Small salamanders and small snakes also are eaten by the Towhee, The Towhee also likes seeds of the Foxtail Grass plants.   When berries are ripe, it eats blackberries, huckleberries, and wild strawberries. Towhees build their nest on or close to the ground. The nest is cup-shaped and well-constructed.  The Towhees migrate south when it gets cold here in our forest. However, when spring comes, they come back to the forest to nest. When I hear that TWEE-TWEE, I know that bird is back.  It is again rummaging through the leaf litter looking for food.

Well, my friend, I must be leaving you now. I hope you will be with me in Book Five. We should see more interesting plants and animals.

We will be delivering the mail to old Zeb. Old Zeb is full of pranks and tricks. Then, we'll deliver mail to Lucky. Lucky is the Yankoo reporter. Jasper, the Yankoo schoolmaster, is also on our route. Finally, we will deliver mail to Sam, our Yankoo judge.

So, Goodbye, my friend! Join me again in Book Five. We will deliver the mail together in our forest.

COTTONTAIL RABBIT

CANADA GOOSE

JUNCO

TURKEY

GRAY SQUIRREL

BEAVER

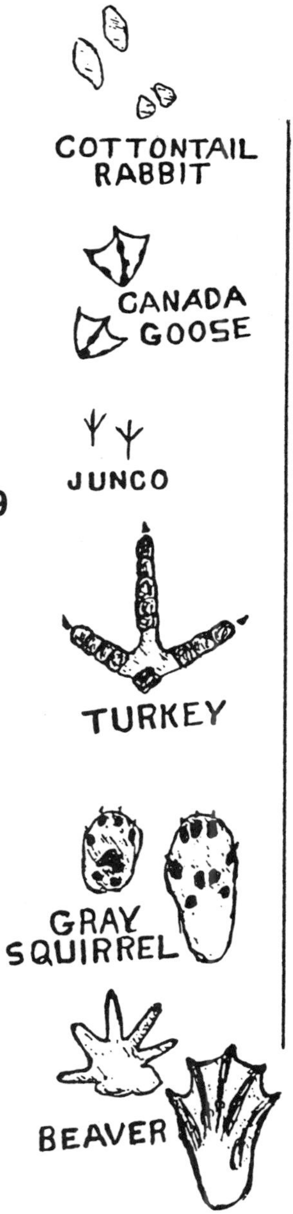

TRACKING IT DOWN

# American Elves - The Yankoos

## The Yankoos and the Oak-Hickory Forest Ecology

This is the fourth in the five book series on plant and animal life in a forest. These books, presenting the wonders of nature in a forest, make ideal gifts for children.

The following four books of the series are now available for purchase. Persons ordering books of the series will be notified when the final book now in preparation, is published.

**Book One:** Illustrated, 64 pages
Soft Cover, 6x9    Cost:    $7.95 postpaid

**Book Two:** Illustrated, 96 pages
Soft Cover, 6x9    Cost:    $7.95 postpaid

**Book Three:** Illustrated, 96 pages
Soft Cover, 6x9    Cost:    $7.95 postpaid

**Book Four:** Illustrated, 96 pages
Soft Cover, 6x9    Cost:    $7.95 postpaid

**Send orders for books to:** Yankoo Publishing Co.
10606 W. Cameo Drive
Sun City, AZ 85351-2708

Make checks payable to:  Yankoo Publishing Co.
Please allow two weeks for U. S. Postal Service delivery.